Pierre TAVERNIERS

Sea ice

LES ÉDITIONS DE L'ESCARGOT SAVANT

*Fast ice and Adélie penguins, 28th November 2011,
Adélie Land, Antarctica © Bertrand Limouzy*

Contents

ILLUSTRATED GUIDE TO SEA ICE

SEA ICE

FAUNA

3

MAN AND THE SEA ICE

Ridge, 16th July 2011, Adélie Land, Antarctica © arr.

Contents

THE DECLINE OF ARCTIC SEA ICE

Ridge and puddle, 2005, Arctic Ocean © Christian Kempf

Hummock, 28th November 2011, Adélie Land, Antarctica © Bertrand Limouzy

ILLUSTRATED GUIDE TO SEA ICE

PRESENTATION

The general definition of sea ice is "all ice from the polar regions caused by the freezing of seawater". But for the purposes of meteorology and sea navigation, there exists a whole range of much more precise definitions. The various national meteorological services keep a close watch on the surface of the oceans, and consequently on sea ice, as part of their mission to protect people and property. In order to ensure the smooth sharing of information internationally, the World Meteorological Organization drew up a glossary called the *Sea-Ice Nomenclature*, containing 170 terms. This glossary distinguishes between **fast ice**, which is attached to the shore, and **drift ice,** which floats on the surface of the water. When concentrations of drift ice are greater than 7/10, the term **pack ice** is generally used.

The first part of this book is an illustrated guide to many of the terms used in the official glossary of sea ice. It explains the numerous and often astonishing ways that sea ice forms, deforms, piles up, breaks apart and melts.

Take a voyage of discovery into this curious world of brash ice, floes, ridges and hummocks.

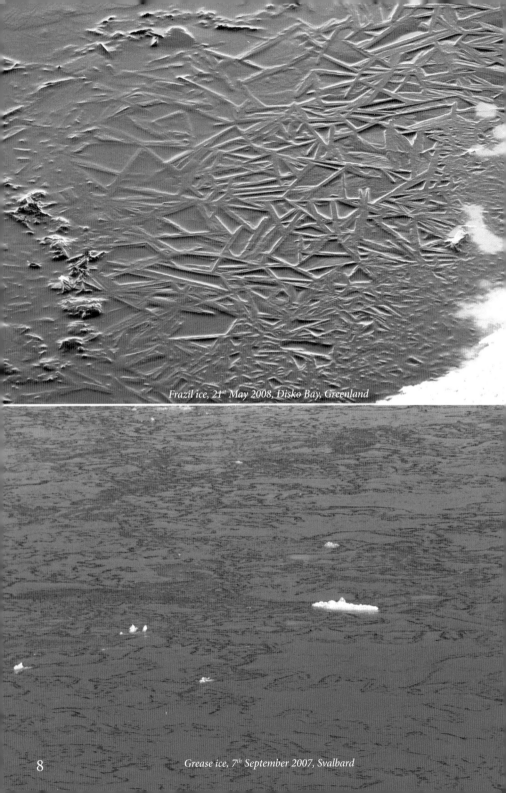

Frazil ice, 21st May 2008, Disko Bay, Greenland

8   *Grease ice, 7th September 2007, Svalbard*

ICE DEVELOPMENT

With an average salt content of 35 grams per litre, the sea starts to freeze when the surface temperature drops to -1.8 °C. But when the salt content is less, such as at the mouth of a river, close to glaciers or icebergs, and particularly in certain fjords littered with ice of land origin, the freezing temperature is closer to 0 °C.

Freezing starts with the formation of thin needle-shaped or flat ice crystals suspended in the water. This is called **frazil ice**. These crystals then begin to clump together to form a thick soupy layer on the surface, called **grease ice**.

Sea ice can also form from **slush**, a viscous mass left floating on the water after a heavy snowfall, or from **shuga**, an accumulation of white spongy lumps of ice a few centimetres across, formed from grease ice or slush.

The term **new ice** covers frazil, grease ice, slush and shuga.

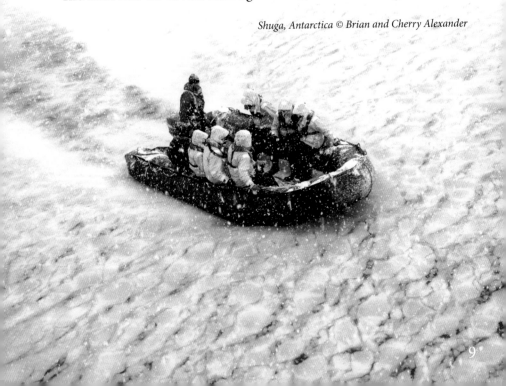

Shuga, Antarctica © Brian and Cherry Alexander

Dark nilas, 23rd March 2011, Adélie Land, Antarctica © Bertrand Limouzy

Young ice, 9th April 2011, Adélie Land, Antarctica © Bertrand Limouzy

The next stage is **nilas,** a thin elastic layer of ice that bends easily on the waves and which may be up to 10 cm thick. **Dark nilas** is less than 5 cm thick, while **light nilas** is more than 5 cm thick.

Ice rind is a shiny brittle crust of ice up to 5 cm thick.

Young ice may be divided into **grey ice** (10 to 15 cm thick) and **grey-white ice** (15 to 30 cm thick).

First-year ice is ice that has formed over just one winter and has a thickness of between 30 cm and two metres. It may be subdivided into **thin first-year ice,** also known as **white ice** (30 to 70 cm thick), **medium first-year ice** (70 to 120 cm thick) and **thick first-year ice** (more than 120 cm thick).

Old ice refers to sea ice that has survived at least one summer melt. Old ice can be as much as three metres thick or more. It can be divided into **second-year ice**, which can be 2.5 metres thick or more in certain cases, and **multi-year ice**, which is three metres thick or more, and has survived at least two summer melts.

Ice rind, 30ᵗʰ August 2011, Arctic © Christian Kempf

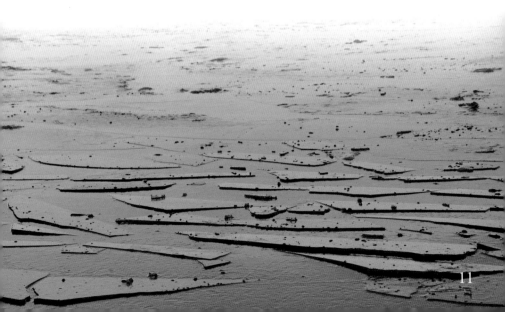

Vast stretch of fast ice, 19th August 2011, Adélie Land, Antarctica © Bertrand Limouzy

Icefoot, 23rd May 2008, Qeqertaq, Greenland

Grounded ice and stranded ice, 3rd August 2009, Resolute, Canada

FAST ICE

Fast ice forms and remains fast along the coast, attached to the shore, to a glacier, or between shoals or grounded icebergs.

Vertical fluctuations may be observed during changes of sea level. Fast ice may be formed in-situ from seawater or by floating ice of any age that freezes to the shore, and it may extend a few metres or several hundred kilometres from the coast.

Fast ice may be more than one year old, in which case it may be prefixed with the appropriate age category: old, second-year or multi-year.

Young coastal ice is formed from nilas or young ice; its width varies from a few metres to 100-200 metres from the shore.

An **ice foot** is a thin strip of ice attached to the shore; it does not move with the tide and remains in place even when the fast ice drifts off.

Anchor ice is ice that's attached or anchored to the sea bottom, irrespective of the nature of its development.

Grounded ice is floating ice that has run aground in shallow water.

Stranded ice is ice that was once floating but has now been deposited on the shore by retreating high water.

Grounded hummocks are hillocks of broken ice, run aground in shallow water. They may stand alone, or form chains.

OCCURENCE AND CONCENTRATION OF FLOATING ICE

The term **ice cover** refers to the ratio of an area of ice (of any concentration) to the total area of sea in some large geographic locality. This locality may be the entire globe, a particular hemisphere or a specific oceanographic entity such as Hudson Bay or the Laptev Sea.

Ice concentration is the ratio (expressed in tenths) of ice-covered sea to non-ice-covered sea in a given area. **Total ice concentration** includes all stages of ice development present. **Partial ice concentration** refers to the amount of a particular stage or of a particular form of ice and represents only a part of the total ice concentration.

Very close ice seen from a satellite, 26ᵗʰ March 2011, Arctic © NASA

Very open ice, 24th July 2010, Svalbard

Floating ice is said to be:
— **compact** when the concentration is 10/10 and no water is visible;
— **consolidated** when the concentration is 10/10 and the floes are frozen together;
— **very close** when the concentration is 9/10 to less than 10/10;
— **close** when the concentration is 7/10 to 8/10 and composed of floes mostly in contact with each other;
— **open** when the concentration is 4/10 to 6/10, with many leads and polynyas, and generally not in contact with each other;
— **very open** when the concentration is 1/10 to 3/10 and there is more water than ice.

Open water means a large area of freely navigable water in which sea ice is present in concentrations of less than 1/10, and no ice of land origin is present.

Bergy water refers to an area of freely navigable water in which ice of land origin is present in concentrations of less than 1/10. There may be sea ice present, but the total concentration of all ice is less than 1/10.

The expression **ice free** means no ice of any kind is present.

15

Pancake ice, 3rd March 2011,
Adélie Land, Antarctica
© Bertrand Limouzy

16

Floe, 7th September 2007, Greenland Sea

FORMS OF FLOATING ICE

Pancake ice refers to circular pieces of ice 30 cm to three metres in diameter and up to 10 cm thick, with raised edges caused by the pieces striking against each other. It may form on a slight swell from grease ice, shuga or slush or as a result of the breaking apart of ice rind, nilas, or even grey ice if the swell or waves are particularly strong. It can sometimes form at depth, at points where water bodies of different physical characteristics meet, after which it floats to the surface. Pancake ice may rapidly form over wide areas of water.

A **floe** is any relatively flat piece of sea ice 20 metres or more across. Floes are subdivided by their horizontal extent into **giant** (greater than 10 km across), **vast** (2 to 10 km across), **big** (500 to 2,000 metres across), **medium** (100 to 500 metres across) and **small** (20 to 100 metres across).

An **ice cake** is any relatively flat piece of sea ice less than 20 metres across. A **small ice cake** is an ice cake less than two metres across.

Ice cake and walruses, 20th August 2005, Svalbard

Floeberg, 24th May 2008, Disko Bay, Greenland

Floebit, 24th July 2010, Svalbard

A **floeberg** is a large piece of sea ice composed of a hummock, or group of hummocks frozen together, separated from any surrounding ice. A floeberg may protrude up to five metres above the surface of the sea.

A **floebit** is a relatively small piece of sea ice, usually not more than ten metres across, composed of one or several hummocks or part of a ridge (or ridges) frozen together and separated from any surrounding ice. It typically protrudes up to two metres above the surface of the sea.

An **ice breccia** is composed of pieces of ice of different stages of development frozen together.

Brash ice is an accumulation of fragments of floating ice (none more than two metres across), essentially the wreckage of other types of ice.

Brash ice, 5th August 2011, Disko Bay, Greenland

Ice field, 17ᵗʰ August 2008, Melville Bay, Greenland

DISTRIBUTION OF ICE

An **ice field** is an area of floating ice floes of any size that stretches for more than 10 km. Ice fields may be subdivided into **large ice fields** (more than 20 km), **medium ice fields** (15 to 20 km) and **small ice fields** (10 to 15 km).

An **ice patch** is an area of floating ice stretching for less than 10 km.

An **ice massif** is an accumulation of close or very close ice covering hundreds of square kilometres and found in the same region every summer.

A **belt** (of ice) is a large area of drift ice, which is longer than it is wide. It may be anything from 1 km to more than 100 km in width.

A **tongue** (of ice) is a projection of the ice edge up to several kilometres long, caused by the wind or the current.

A **strip** (of ice) is a long narrow area of floating ice, one kilometre long or less, and usually composed of small fragments detached from the main ice mass, which are brought together by the effects of wind, swell or current.

An **ice isthmus** is a narrow connection between two areas of very close or compact ice. It may be difficult to cross, while sometimes being part of a recommended route.

A **bight** is an extensive crescent-shaped indentation in the ice edge, formed by either wind or current.

An **ice jam** is an accumulation of broken sea ice blocking a narrow waterway.

The ice edge is the demarcation, at any given time, between the open sea and any kind of sea ice, be it fast or drifting. A compacted ice edge is one that is clearly defined by compaction from wind or current, usually on the windward side of an area of drift ice. A diffuse ice edge is a poorly defined ice edge delimiting an area of dispersed floating ice, usually on the leeward side of an area of drift ice.

A jammed brash barrier is a narrow strip of new, young or brash ice, generally 100 to 5,000 metres wide, that has formed at the edge of either drift ice, fast ice, or at the shore. Heavily compacted, mainly by the wind, these features may extend 2 to 20 metres below the surface of the water, but have no appreciable topography. Jammed brash barriers may be dispersed by changing winds, but may also consolidate and form a strip of unusually thick ice compared with the surrounding drift ice.

Fast ice edge, 29th December 2011,
Adélie Land, Antarctica © Bertrand Limouzy

The **ice limit** is a climatological term for the extreme minimum or maximum extent of the ice edge in any given month or period, based on observations made over a number of years. This term should always be preceded by *minimum* or *maximum*.

The **mean ice edge** is the average position of the ice edge in any given month or period, based on observations made over a number of years. Other terms that may be used are **mean maximum ice edge** and **mean minimum ice edge**.

The **fast ice edge** is the boundary between fast ice and open water at any given time.

The **ice boundary** is the boundary between fast ice and drift ice, or between areas of drift ice of different concentrations at any given time.

The **fast ice boundary** is the boundary between fast ice and drift ice at any given time.

The **concentration boundary** is a line marking the approximate transition between two areas of drift ice of clearly different concentrations.

23

Crack in the fast ice, 6ᵗʰ June 2011,
Adélie Land, Antarctica © Bertrand Limouzy

OPENINGS IN THE ICE

A **fracture** refers to any break or rupture in very close ice, compact ice, consolidated ice, fast ice or a single floe, resulting from deformation phenomena. Fractures may contain brash ice or be covered with nilas or young ice. They may be anything from a few metres to a few kilometres long. Fractures are subdivided into **very small fractures** (1 to 50 metres wide), **small fractures** (50 to 200 metres wide), **medium factures** (200 to 500 metres wide) and **large fractures** (more than 500 metres wide).

A **crack** is any fracture in fast ice, consolidated ice or a single floe, followed by a separation of several centimetres to a metre.

A **tide crack** is a crack at the junction between an immovable ice foot or ice wall and fast ice, the latter subject to the rise and fall of the tide.

Very small fracture in a floe © Bernard Lefauconnier

Polynya refers to any non-linear opening enclosed by ice. Polynyas may contain brash ice or be covered with new ice, nilas or young ice. A **shore polynya** is one situated between drift ice and the shore or between drift ice and an ice front. A **flaw polynya** is one situated between drift ice and fast ice. **Recurring polynyas** reappear in the same place each year.

Polynya, 5th April 2011, Adélie Land, Antarctica © arr.

A **lead** is a fracture or passage through sea ice that is navigable by a surface vessel. A **shore lead** is a passage between drift ice and the shore or an ice front, while a **flaw lead** connects drift ice and fast ice.

A **flaw** is a narrow separation zone between drift ice and fast ice, where the pieces of ice are in a chaotic state. It forms when drift ice shears along the fast ice boundary under the effect of a strong wind or current.

Flaw, 7ᵗʰ April 2003, Arctic © Bernard Lefauconnier

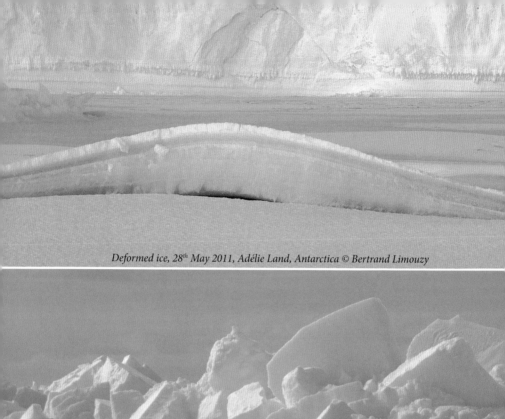

Deformed ice, 28th May 2011, Adélie Land, Antarctica © Bertrand Limouzy

New ridge, 8th June 2008, Arctic © Bernard Lefauconnier

Weathered ridge, 21st August 2005, Arctic Ocean

ICE SURFACE FEATURES

Level ice is sea ice without any visible deformation.

Deformed ice is a general term referring to ice that has been squeezed together and forced upward or downward in places.
It may be subdivided into rafted ice, ridged ice and hummocked ice.

Rafted ice is formed by one piece of ice riding up over another.

Finger rafted ice occurs when rafting floes interlace to create a formation resembling interlocking fingers.

A **ridge** is a line or wall of broken ice forced up by pressure, and there are several different types.
A **new ridge** is characterized by sharp peaks and steeply sloping sides.
A **weathered ridge** has rounded peaks and more gently sloping sides.
Very weathered ridges are even more rounded, and **aged ridges** are little more than undulations.
A **consolidated ridge** is where the base has frozen completely.
An **ice keel** is the downward-projecting submerged underside of a ridge. Ice keels may extend as far as 50 metres below the surface.

Ridged ice is ice piled up haphazardly to form ridges or walls.

A **shear ridge** is a ridge formed by the sliding of two sections of the ice against each other.

Hummock, 12th August 2011, Arctic Ocean

Hummocked ice, 31st August 2011, Adélie Land, Antarctica © Bertrand Limouzy

A **hummock** is a hillock of broken ice that has been forced upwards by pressure. It may be fresh or weathered. The volume of broken ice submerged beneath a hummock is called a **bummock.**

Hummocked ice is ice piled up haphazardly to form an uneven surface. When weathered, it has the appearance of rounded hillocks.

A **rubble field** is an area of extremely deformed sea ice of unusual thickness formed during the winter by the motion of drift ice against an obstruction such as a rock or islet.

A **standing floe** is an upright or inclined pinnacle of ice, standing in isolation and surrounded by generally smooth ice.

Standing floe, 16th May 2011,
Adélie Land, Antarctica © Bertrand Limouzy

Ram, 7th September 2007, Arctic © Christian Kempf

A **ram** is an underwater projection from a floe, generally caused by more intense melting and weathering of the ice above the surface of the water.

Bare ice is ice not covered by snow.

Sastrugi are sharp, irregular ridges formed on a snow-covered surface by wind erosion and deposition.

A **snowdrift** is an accumulation of snow deposited in the lee of obstructions or piled up by wind eddies. A crescent-shaped snowdrift, the ends of which point downwind, is called a **snow barchan**.

Snowdrift, 7ᵗʰ September 2011, Adélie Land, Antarctica © Bertrand Limouzy

Vortex in the new ice of a fracture, 28th May 2011, Adélie Land, Antarctica © Bertrand Limouzy

Effect of freezing and wind on a puddle, 3rd June 2011, Adélie Land, Antarctica © Bertrand Limouzy

Broken ice on the surface of a puddle, 20th August 2005, Arctic © Christian Kempf

Light nilas folded by pressure, 3rd April 2011, Adélie Land, Antarctica © Bertrand Limouzy

Puddle, 24ᵗʰ July 2005, Arctic © Bernard Lefauconnier

MELT STAGES

A **puddle** is an accumulation of water on the ice, mainly formed by melting snow, but also, in its more advanced stages, from the melting of the ice itself.

Thaw holes are vertical holes in ice formed when surface puddles melt through to the underlying sea.

Dried ice is a surface of ice from which all meltwater has drained, usually through cracks and thaw holes. As the ice dries, it whitens.

Rotten ice is sea ice so riddled by thaw holes that it has started to disintegrate.

Flooded ice is sea ice that has been inundated by meltwater or river water, or become heavily loaded with wet snow.

Shore melt refers to open water between the coast and fast ice resulting from melted ice or river water.

Rotten ice, 2nd August 2006, Smith Sound, Arctic

Break-up with a 170 km/h wind, 23ʳᵈ April 2011, Adélie Land, Antarctica © Bertrand Limouzy

BREAK-UP

The term break-up also refers to the thawing and rupture of ice covering a watercourse. Break-ups on major rivers, notably in Siberia, are often spectacular, involving millions of cubic metres of ice, carrying away parts of the shoreline and flooding whole regions.

Break-up, 14ᵗʰ June 2008,
Arctic © Bernard Lefauconnier

BREAK-UP

The term **break-up** applies mainly to fast ice. A break-up occurs when sea ice is broken apart by wind or the swell. Break-up usually occurs in autumn when the ice is just forming and so is thin and not very strong. As winter bites, the cold deepens, and the ice thickens and becomes increasingly stronger, making break-up less frequent and generally limited to unsheltered stretches of coast in windy regions. This is the case in Antarctica, where the katabatic winds from the ice sheet are particularly violent, often exceeding 150 km/h. A katabatic wind, also called a fall wind, is one carrying high-density air down a slope under the force of gravity. In autumn and winter, the sea freezes again and the sea ice reforms once the wind dies down. Successive periods of freezing and break-up can result in a stretch of sea ice composed of multiple sections at different stages of development, known as an **ice breccia**. Come spring, the rise in air and sea temperatures causes the surface and the base of the sea ice to melt, gradually reducing its strength. The floes resulting from a break-up generally have a characteristic shape with straight edges.

Break-up, 14th June 2008, Arctic © Bernard Lefauconnier

CHARTING SEA ICE

The meteorological services of certain countries such as Canada, Denmark, Norway, Russia and Finland produce ice charts so that shipping routes can be planned and navigated safely.

These charts may be produced daily or on an irregular basis, they may cover small regions or very large areas, but all are drafted in accordance with the international codes drawn up by the World Meteorological Organization. They are mainly ice analysis charts based on observations made using satellites, aircraft, ships or coastal stations.

Some charts, such as those drawn up by the Norwegian Meteorological Institute, show the distribution of ice at sea and its concentration expressed in tenths, using colour codes starting with blue for open water right up to red for very close ice. Fast ice is depicted in dark grey.

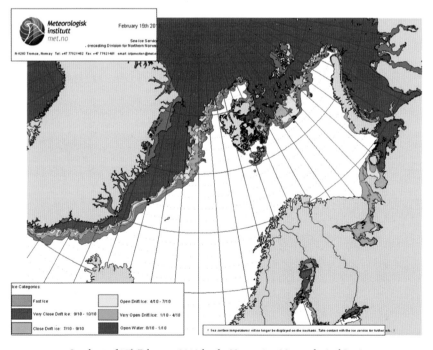

Ice chart of 15ᵗʰ February 2013 by the Norwegian Meteorological Institute

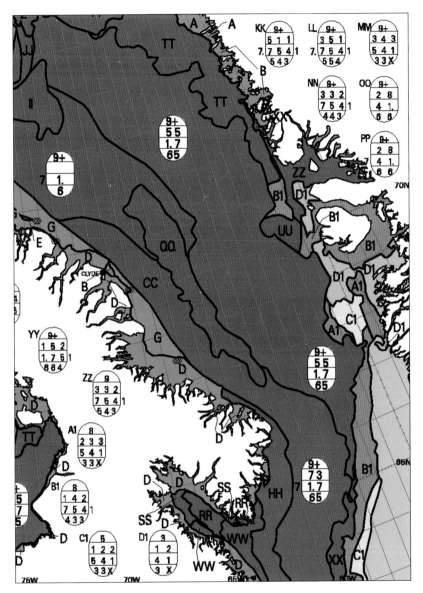

Detail from the ice chart of 28th January 2013 by the Canadian Ice Service

Other charts, such as those drawn up by the Canadian Ice Service, also show stages of development (nilas, old ice, etc.) and forms of ice (pancake ice, floe, etc.) in addition to distribution and concentration. The information is presented using the **egg code**.

41

EGG CODE

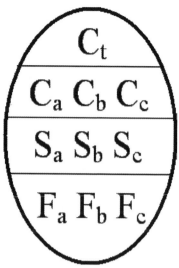

Ct is the total concentration of ice in the sector, expressed in tenths.

Ca, Cb and **Cc** are the partial concentrations of ice, expressed in tenths and ranked from left to right (where **Ca** is the thickest and **Cc** is the thinnest).

Sa, Sb and **Sc** are the corresponding stages of development for **Ca, Cb** and **Cc**.

Fa, Fb and **Fc** are the corresponding forms of ice for **Sa, Sb** and **Sc**.

When there are more than three concentrations, three stages of development or three forms of ice to be described, additional letters are placed to the right of the oval: **Cd + Ce, Sd + Se, Fd + Fe**.

Four letters may be added below the oval to indicate the thickness concentration of any brash ice present: V designates a thickness greater than four metres, K represents thickness ranging from two to four metres, M represents one to two metres, and T indicates less than one metre.

Emperor penguins and egg,
May 2006, Adélie Land, Antarctica
© Samuel Blanc

Stages of development of sea ice (**Sa, Sb, Sc, Sd, Se**)

CODE	DESCRIPTION	THICKNESS
1	New ice	< 10 cm
2	Nilas, ice rind	< 10 cm
3	Young ice	10 - 30 cm
4	Grey ice	10 - 15 cm
5	Grey-white ice	15 - 30 cm
6	First-year ice	> = 30 cm
7	Thin first-year ice	30 - 70 cm
8	Thin first-year ice, first stage	30 - 50 cm
9	Thin first-year ice, second stage	50 - 70 cm
1.	Medium first-year ice	70 - 120 cm
4.	Thick first-year ice	> 120 cm
7.	Old ice	-
8.	Second-year ice	-
9.	Multi-year ice	-
.	Ice of land origin	-
x.	Undetermined or unknown	-

Forms of ice (**Fa, Fb, Fc, Fd, Fe**)

CODE	DESCRIPTION	SIZE
0	Pancake ice	-
1	Small ice cake, brash ice	< two metres
2	Ice cake	2 to 20 metres
3	Small floe	20 - 100 metres
4	Medium floe	100 - 500 metres
5	Big floe	500 – 2,000 metres
6	Vast floe	2 to 10 km
7	Giant floe	> 10 km
8	Fast ice	-
9	Icebergs, floebergs	-
x	Undetermined, unknown or no form	-

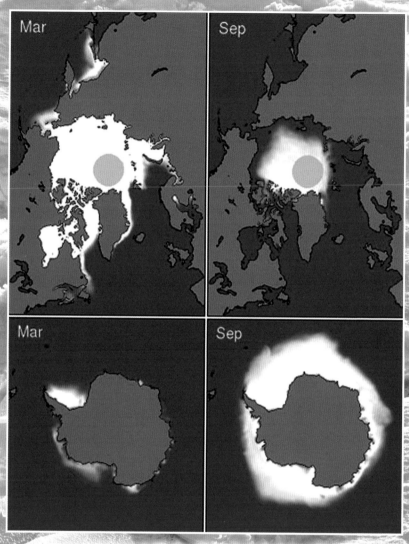

Average extent of sea ice in March and September in the Arctic and Antarctica, calculated for the period 1978-2007.

SEA ICE

EXTENT AND AREA

Observations concerning the extent of sea ice were irregular and patchy until 1978, when regular and consistent satellite observations commenced. By 2008, the data collected provided scientists with a record of sea ice climatology spanning thirty years.

In the Arctic, the maximum extent of sea ice occurs in March, covering an average area of 15 million km^2. The minimum extent occurs in September, covering an average area of 7 million km^2.

In winter, the ice cover is dissymmetrical in relation to the Geographic North Pole. On the Pacific side, sea ice stretches as far as the north of Japan, at 45°N, 5,000 km from the Pole. On the Atlantic side, sea ice extends no further than 78°N on the west coast of Spitsbergen, 1,300 km from the Pole.

In summer, ice remains in the heart of the Arctic Basin as well as between the northern islands of the Canadian Arctic Archipelago.

In the Arctic, a significant reduction in the extent of sea ice was observed over the period 1978-2007. The reduction was more pronounced in summer than in winter (see the last part of this book devoted to the decline of Arctic sea ice).

In Antarctica, the maximum extent of sea ice occurs in September, reaching an average area of 18 million km^2. The minimum extent occurs in March, with an average area of 3 million km^2.

In winter, ice cover is quite symmetrical in relation to the Geographic South Pole. Sea ice extends as far as latitude 63°S on the Antarctic Peninsula and 55°S in the Atlantic, that is to say 3,000 to 3,900 km from the pole.

In summer, drift ice remains principally in the Weddell Sea and from the Ross Sea to the Bellinghausen Sea.

In Antarctica, an increase in the extent of sea ice of 0.9% per decade was observed over the period 1978-2007.

THICKNESS AND SALINITY

Sea ice thickens according to air temperature. At a temperature of -10 °C, ice may thicken by 3-5 cm in the first 24 hours. At -20 °C to -30 °C, it may reach 8-10 cm. Thickening slows from that point because thicker ice insulates the ocean from the atmosphere. At -30 °C, thickness may attain 40 cm in two weeks. At -50 °C, it may reach two metres in two months. But ice cannot thicken indefinitely, and at -50 °C maximum thickness is about three metres. However, in addition to thickening from the freezing of seawater, further thickening may be caused by winter snowfalls and the subsequent melting and refreezing of snow during the summer. A vertical slice of old ice extracted from the Arctic Ocean in 1954 (Chomsky) displayed the following layers from top to bottom: 10 cm of snow, 40 cm of refrozen ice, 110 cm of sea ice over four years old, 130 cm of sea ice under four years old.

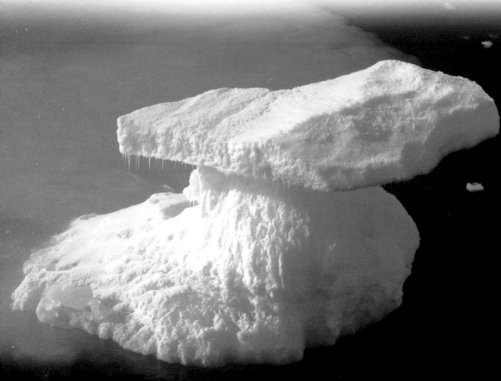

A block of sea ice progressively loses its salt once out of the water, 7ᵗʰ September 2007, Greenland Sea

Tractor and trailer on fast ice. The long tow rope allows the load to be spread better and reduces the risk of breaking the ice, 19th August 2011, Adélie Land, Antarctica © Bertrand Limouzy

This data concerns non-deformed level ice. When ice piles up into hummocks, the thickness of this rafted ice may be as much as eight to ten metres above the surface of the sea and more than 20 metres beneath it.

Snow on the surface of ice plays an important role, not only as an insulator but also through its weight. Heavy snowfall can push ice down into the sea, causing seawater to flood up onto its surface.

The capacity of sea ice to support a load (bearing capacity) depends both on air temperature and also the occurrence of cracks. The recommended sea ice thickness to support the weight of a person is a dozen centimetres. To support the weight of a three-ton vehicle, the recommended thickness is around 50 cm at a temperature of -2 °C, and 28 cm at a temperature of -15 °C. For a thirty-ton vehicle the recommended thickness is 180 cm at -2 °C and 110 cm at -15 °C.

When seawater freezes, ice crystals are squeezed downwards. This process continues as the ice thickens, to such an extent that old ice may contain no salt at all at its surface. In summer, the puddles on the surface of old ice are therefore composed of fresh water. A block of first-year sea ice removed from the water and exposed to melting will end up containing no salt.

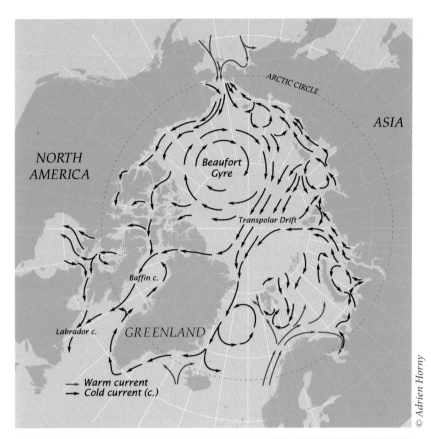

ARCTIC CIRCLE

ASIA

NORTH
AMERICA

Beaufort
Gyre

Transpolar Drift

Baffin c.

Labrador c.   GREENLAND

→ Warm current
➤ Cold current (c.)

© Adrien Horny

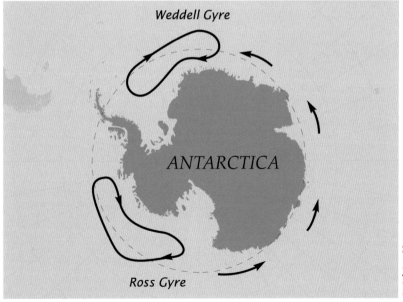

Weddell Gyre

ANTARCTICA

Ross Gyre

© Adrien Horny

CURRENTS

In the Arctic, the ice which forms in the centre of the Arctic Basin is initially carried by the Beaufort Gyre, then by the Transpolar Drift Stream before entering the North Atlantic.

Some of this ice follows the East Greenland Current and may reach southwest Greenland. The configuration of the Arctic Ocean allows ice to spend several years, sometimes as long as six or seven, in the Central Basin before reaching the North Atlantic.

This is the oldest and thickest sea ice on our planet. Drift speeds are about 6 km a day in the centre of the Arctic Basin and may reach 50 km a day at the exit from the basin.

Surface winds caused by passing depressions can affect the direction and speed of the ice's movement. Sea ice in the Arctic Ocean is constantly moving, bringing floes crashing together, rafting over each other, piling up into hummocks or breaking apart.

It's the reason why reaching the North Pole via a surface route is so difficult. One can very easily lose all the ground covered in a day as the ice drifts overnight.

In Antarctica, ice can spend one or two years in the gyres of the Weddell Sea and the Ross Sea. The configuration of Antarctica, a continent surrounded by oceans, does not allow ice to age and thicken as much as in the Arctic.

British explorer Ernest Shackleton's 1914-1917 expedition spent 450 days drifting with the ice of the Weddell Sea for 900 km.

CLIMATIC ROLE

Sea ice plays a major role in our planet's climate.

Firstly, it acts as a reflector of solar energy, mainly in spring and summer. Sea ice covered with fresh snow can reflect 75-90% of solar energy, whereas the surface of the open sea reflects just 5-15%.

Secondly, sea ice acts as an insulator, mainly in autumn and winter. This insulating effect limits the amount of both heat and moisture the ocean loses to the atmosphere.

Sea ice also has an effect on ocean circulation. When sea ice forms, salt is squeezed to the base of the ice, making very salty, cold, dense water that sinks to the ocean floor, to be replaced at the surface by warmer water flowing from lower latitudes. This circulation, caused by temperature and salinity differences, is called **thermohaline circulation** and helps to distribute the oceans' heat around the globe.

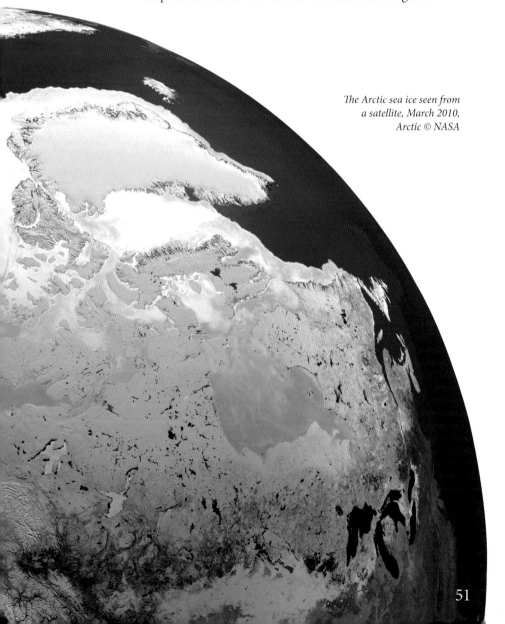

The Arctic sea ice seen from a satellite, March 2010, Arctic © NASA

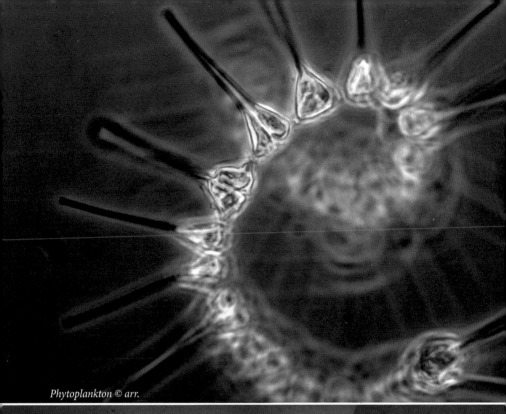

Phytoplankton © arr.

Jellyfish under the sea ice © arr.

LIFE IN THE ICE

During winter, the snow-covered sea ice keeps the underlying water in darkness. Come spring, the melting snow allows sunlight to reach the ice, causing microscopic algae to develop both beneath and in the sea ice. The rapid lengthening of days and increase in melting of the ice leads to a spectacular growth of these algae, a phenomenon called a phytoplankton bloom, that is sometimes visible from space. These algae are associated with microscopic organisms and form what is called a sympagic ecosystem; one where water exists mainly as a solid. The phytoplankton are eaten by zooplankton, making the basis of a food chain including fish, birds, sea mammals and, in the Arctic, polar bears.

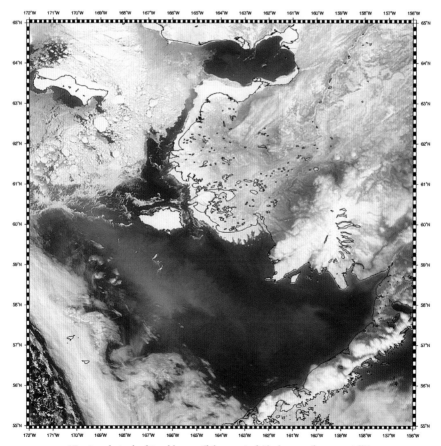

Massive phytoplankton bloom off the coast of Alaska seen from a satellite, 29ᵗʰ April 2000 © NASA

53

Polar bear © *Christian Kempf*

FAUNA

THE ARCTIC

The emblematic animal of the Arctic sea ice is the **polar bear** (*Ursus maritimus*). Adult polar bears measure two to three metres from nose to tail, with females weighing 150 to 295 kg and males 350 to 540 kg. They mainly eat seals, which they only capture on the ice. The Inuit call the polar bear *pisuttualuk* (the great wanderer). Polar bears roam the sea ice looking for seals, which are generally found near coasts and on the continental shelves. They wait at a seal's breathing hole, and when it emerges, kill it with a single swipe of their claws. A polar bear has an extremely keen sense of smell, allowing it to detect a seal dozens of kilometres away. Its long neck also helps it to survey its surroundings, while its white fur provides camouflage against the snow and ice. Polar bears stalk seals by hiding behind ridges and hummocks, and can reach speeds of 40 km/h and leap seven metres, stunning their prey with their considerable body mass. A polar bear can smell a seal's den located beneath a snowdrift and smash in the roof using its front paws like a sledgehammer. Capable of swimming for hundreds of kilometres, polar bears also hunt seals resting on ice floes, diving underwater to hide before surging up onto the edge of a floe to surprise the animal. Polar bears reproduce on the ice. Females give birth in a den dug into young snow known as névé. The dens are situated on the coast, close enough to the sea ice so that after six months of fasting, during which she will have given birth and suckled her young, the mother can find seals to catch as quickly as possible. When first-year ice disappears in spring, many polar bears remain on the coasts. They survive by eating birds, eggs and vegetation and can fast for several weeks until the ice returns, although they will lose weight in doing so. In years when sea ice disappears too early in spring and returns too late in autumn, females are unable to reproduce as they lack sufficient fat reserves to make it through the winter.

Ribbon seal, June 2012, Sea of Okhotsk
© *Christian Kempf*

The **ringed seal** (*Phoca hispida*) measures 1.2 to 1.5 metres and weighs 60 to 100 kg. It's the smallest species of seal in the Arctic, but also the one with the largest population, estimated at six or seven million. The female prefers thick ice and gives birth in a den she digs in a snowdrift, the only entrance to which is through a hole dug in the sea ice. In winter, the ringed seal uses the claws on its front flippers to dig breathing holes in first-year ice up to two metres thick. During the moulting period, which runs from mid-May to mid-July, ringed seals usually remain on the surface of the sea ice.

The **harp seal** (*Phoca Greenlandica*) measures 1.5 to 2 metres and weighs 100 to 150 kg. It is also called *Pagophilus*, meaning "one who likes the ice". This species reproduces and moults on the sea ice, entering the water through cracks or fractures. Harp seals give birth in late-February/ early-March, when the sea ice is at maximum extent. When the sea ice is regionally absent or reduced to brash ice, they give birth in the water and the newborns drown. But if they are born on sea ice, the young, more commonly known as whitecoats, can enter the water ten days after birth. The whitecoat has become *the* symbol of the campaigns undertaken by conservation charities to obtain a prohibition on seal hunting.

The **ribbon seal** (*Phoca fasciata*) measures around 1.75 metres and weighs 90 kg. This species reproduces and moults on the sea ice. The ribbon seal makes breathing holes in the ice and has the ability to move quickly across the ice surface. The species is only found in the Sea of Okhotsk, the Bering Sea, the Chukchi Sea and the western part of the Beaufort Sea.

The **bearded seal** (*Erignathus barbatus*) measures 2 to 2.5 metres and weighs 250 to 350 kg. It generally favours floating ice, and although it can dig breathing holes, does so only in ice that is fairly thin, no more than a dozen centimetres. Females give birth on the ice and their young can swim as soon as they are born.

Bearded seal, August 2011, Svalbard © Laurent Balp

The **hooded seal** (*Cystophora cristata*) measures 1.8 to 2.2 metres (female) and 2.5 to 3 metres (male), with respective weights of 180 to 400 kg. This species reproduces and moults on the sea ice. The young can swim from birth.

The **spotted seal** (*Phoca largha*) measures 1.5 to 1.7 metres and weighs 80 to 90 kg. This species gives birth on the sea ice but cannot dig breathing holes and so lives at the ice edge, on ice cakes or small floes. The spotted seal may be found anywhere on the ice from the Sea of Okhotsk to the north of the Bering Strait.

The **walrus** (*Odobenus rosmarus*) measures 2.5 to 2.6 metres (female) and 3 to 3.6 metres (male), with respective weights of 750 to 1,600 kg. The walrus is a coastal animal that lives on floes or spends winter close to polynyas. *Odobenus* means "that walks on teeth", although walruses mainly use their long tusks to pull themselves out of the water onto the ice.

The **ivory gull** (*Pagophila eburnéa*) is the only species in the genus *Pagophila*, meaning "which likes the ice". It lives on the sea ice, but reproduces on land close to the ice. The ivory gull is a carrion-eater that feeds mainly on seal carcasses abandoned by polar bears. If there is no meat around, it will scavenge through excrement left on the ice by polar bears, walruses and seals.

Ivory gulls, July 2010, Svalbard © Laurent Balp

Walrus, August 2008, Svalbard © Laurent Balp

ANTARCTICA

The **emperor penguin** (*Aptenodytes forsteri*) measures 1.1 to 1.3 metres and weighs 23 to 38 kg according to sex and season. This animal reproduces on fast ice, close to the continent, preferably between islands where the sea ice is level and most resistant to break-up). In March/April, adult mating pairs travel to reproduction sites. They leave the open sea and move across the ice, either walking or else sliding on their belly, pushing themselves along with their flippers and feet. Emperor penguins may have to cover more than 100 km according to the extent of the fast ice. In May, the female lays a single egg, which she entrusts to the male to incubate. The transfer of the egg is a delicate affair, since the egg must not remain exposed to the freezing air for long, nor must it touch the ice. Level ice is therefore required for a successful transfer! The egg is placed on the male's feet, then covered by his brood pouch. Having fasted for 40 days, the females return to the sea to feed, while the males remain standing on the ice for two months incubating the eggs. During this period the temperature can drop as low as -35 °C and winds can reach

Emperor penguin, 2006,
Adélie Land, Antarctica
© Samuel Blanc

Weddell seal in its breathing hole, 2006,
Adélie Land, Antarctica © Samuel Blanc

speeds of 100 km/h, resulting in a wind chill temperature of -60 °C. To survive such harsh conditions and keep heat loss to a minimum, the males huddle together, constantly moving so that each individual gets to spend time in the centre of the huddle where the temperature remains above zero. The chicks are born in July, and although the males can feed them with a regurgitated curd-like substance, it only last a few days, so it is vital the females return in time to take over feeding duties. When they do, the males can finally leave to feed. Famished after four months without food, they make use of any opening in the ice, be it a polynya, a fracture or a seal breathing hole, to reach the sea as quickly as possible. The chick spends 35 to 40 days in the brood pouch, with the parents taking turns to feed it. In early November, the chick loses its down and acquires what is called its juvenile plumage, and is ready to leave the colony by late November or early December, coinciding with the start of the break-up of the sea ice. The emperor penguin's reproductive cycle follows the development/break-up cycle of the sea ice, so that the young leave the colony in springtime when the waters are richer in nutrients, before enjoying a whole summer over which to feed and grow. But their survival depends on the state of the fast ice. Fast ice that extends very far without any opening compels the adults to search much further afield for food, and stay away much longer, increasing the danger of chicks dying through undernourishment and overexposure to harsh weather. An early break-up of the sea ice can force the chicks into the water and result in them drowning.

The **Weddell seal** (*Leptonychotes weddelli*) measures 2.6 to 3.2 metres and weighs 300 to 400 kg. This generally coastal animal reproduces on the ice and can dig breathing holes with its teeth, although it also uses fractures in the sea ice. Births take place from mid-October to mid-November and weaning, six to seven weeks later. Early break-up of the fast ice can result in a high mortality rate among the young pups.

The **Ross seal** (*Ommatophoca rossi*) measures 2 to 2.5 metres and weighs 170 kg on average. This is the smallest species in Antarctica.

Leopard seal, 2006,
Adélie Land, Antarctica
© Samuel Blanc

Weddell seal, 2011,
Adélie Land, Antarctica
© arr.

The name *Omma-*
tophoca comes from
the Greek *omma* (eye), since this
animal's eye sockets are disproportionately large in relation to the size of
its head, hence its other nickname of big-eyed seal. This species favours
drift ice, with births occurring on the ice in November and December,
and weaning taking four to six weeks.

The **crabeater seal** (*Lobodon carcinophagus*) measures 2.6 metres
and weighs 225 kg. It has finely lobed teeth (hence *Lobodon*) that allow
it to filter krill. The crabeater seal favours drift ice and can move rapidly
across the surface at speeds of up to 25 km/h. Births take place on the
ice in September and October and weaning occurs two to four weeks
later. This is the most populous species of seal in the world, with an
estimated 13 million individuals.

The **leopard seal** (*Hydrurga leptonyx*) measures three metres (male)
and up to 3.7 metres (female), and generally weighs 270 to 300 kg, although some can reach 500 kg. Leopard Seals favour drift ice. Births
take place from September to January, with mothers remaining on the
ice with their young and suckling them for about a month. The leopard
seal is a fearsome predator that hunts in the water and sometimes on the
ice. It is capable of surging out of the sea and sliding across the ice for
several metres to attack penguins.

Weddell seal, 2011, Adélie Land, Antarctica © Bertrand Limouzy

64

Harp seals, © Alain Desbrosse

Dog sled near Qeqertaq, 1988, Greenland

MAN AND THE SEA ICE

THE INUIT

An historic ice route

Sometime between 2,000 and 8,000 years ago, nomadic hunters from eastern Siberia crossed the Bering Strait and reached North America. These Paleo-Eskimo continued along the coasts of Alaska to the Canadian Arctic Archipelago and then on to Greenland, in the course of several migrations by way of the sea ice that acted as a bridge between the islands. Towards 1000 CE, the Thule people, ancestors of the modern Inuit, began to expand eastward from Alaska, reaching Greenland by 1300 CE. The last Inuit migration from Canada to Greenland over the sea ice took place in the mid-19th century.

Different types of sea ice

The Inuit, who are mainly hunters of sea mammals, are spread across some 15,000 km of Arctic coast at northern latitudes between 54° and 77°, and so encounter a wide range of types of sea ice. The sea around southern Greenland freezes only rarely, but the Inuit who live there do see drift ice. The most northern Inuit experience up to 11 months of fast ice per year, which can be up to two metres thick, while the Nunavimiut of Ungava Bay (Canada) experience the greatest deformations of fast ice due to tidal ranges of up to 15 metres. As for the Tunumiit of eastern Greenland, they see the oldest and thickest drift ice, which comes from the Arctic Ocean.

Dog sled on the sea ice, 1988, Qeqertaq, Greenland

Travel

The coast is often craggy and crossed by glaciers, but fast ice is generally level, making it practical for travel, ideally using a **dog sled**. This is an economical means of transport because the sleds are built locally and the dogs are fed with what the Inuit hunt and fish. Dog sledding is not only well suited to long journeys, but also to communal travel. Even recently, it was not uncommon for communities of a hundred people living on the northwest coast of Greenland to travel across the sea ice by dog sled to visit other communities, sometimes more than 100 km away. These visits were occasion for celebrations and games, and strengthened the links between communities. Today, the dog sled is mainly used in the northwest and east of Greenland.

Hunting

Fast ice is a hunting ground where it's often easier to catch marine mammals than on the open sea. Seals may be caught as they emerge from breathing holes, or when they are resting on

Hunting a seal at a breathing hole
© Enook Manomie

Seal-hunting with a net laid under the ice, 1988, Qeqertaq, Greenland

the ice. The Inuit of western Greenland practise a form of seal hunting that was developed in the 19th century, using nets set underneath the ice. White whales and narwhals are easily captured when trapped in a polynya, the only place they can surface to breathe. Fast ice is also the best place to hunt polar bears, since the animal is more easily pursued than amid the drift ice. Come springtime, the Inuit also hunt the migrating birds that set down at polynyas in large numbers, often returning to the same spots year on year. The edge of fast ice is also a favourite hunting spot for the Inuit, since this is where many sea mammals emerge from the water.

The senior hunter has caught a seal, 1988, Qeqertaq, Greenland

Fishing

The Inuit used to fish with a harpoon, either by making a hole in the ice or else through cracks or fractures. Fishing, which has become the main source of income in Greenland, is now practised using long lines laid underneath the ice. The Nunavimiut of Ungava Bay sometimes slip beneath the fast ice at low tide to harvest mussels.

Harpoon fishing
© Enook Manomie

Qeqertamiut haul away a block of sea ice they cut out to lay a fishing line, 1988, Greenland

Qeqertamiut removing blocks of fresh water ice from an iceberg, 1988, Greenland

Access to fresh water

Communities without a lake or river close by can get fresh water by hacking blocks of ice from icebergs trapped by the sea ice.

A community space

The sea ice is also the stage for Inuit gatherings, games and dog sled or snowmobile racing, which serve to maintain community cohesion and settle disputes.

Dog sled races on the sea ice, 1988, Qeqertaq, Greenland

A learning space

Young Inuit accompany adults onto the sea ice to learn through observation and teaching the knowledge and techniques associated with sea ice.

Access to resources

Some Inuit, particularly the elders, don't possess boats in which to hunt and fish at sea during the summer, but they can count on community solidarity. The sea ice allows everyone, elders, women and children to access the marine resources.

Preservation of identity

The sea ice allows the Inuit to continue their ancestral ways of moving about, hunting, fishing and playing. The manufacture of fur clothing suited to living on the sea ice is yet another way they preserve their identity.

Hunter untangling the reins of his dog-sled harness, 1988, Qeqertaq, Greenland

The sea ice is both playground and classroom for Inuit children, 1988, Qeqertaq, Greenland

At home on the drift ice

An unexpected break-up of fast ice, perhaps due to a storm, can set the Inuit adrift on a floe. Tales passed down orally from generation to generation recount such misadventures and highlight the capacity for adaptation of the Inuit, their endurance in the face of cold and hunger, and the ingenuity that has allowed them to survive in such situations. Indeed this is how they discovered new islands, new lands and fantastic creatures.

73

Inuit cutting up their catch on a floe,
Kulusuk, Greenland © Samuel Blanc

But the Inuit willingly set out among the drift
ice in their kayaks or canoes. When they catch a 300 kg
hooded seal, or a walrus weighing more than a ton, the hunters set
foot on a solid floe, drag their prize onto the ice, and cut it into smaller
pieces, making it easier to carry home aboard their boats.

In Alaska, the Inupiat hunt North Atlantic right whales (*Eubalaena
glacialis*) during their seasonal migration from Greenland. Hunters
from a particular community form teams that take up position amid
the drift ice in their canoes or umiaqs, traditional boats made of wood
and the skins of marine mammals. They make temporary camps on
old-ice floes, which are the strongest, and from there they spot passing
whales. When a whale has been harpooned it is dragged close to shore,
hauled onto land using ropes and pulleys, and then shared between all
the members of the community.

Kiŋikmi Sigum Qanuq Ilitaavut

Wales Iñupiaq Sea Ice Dictionary

Knowledge

The Inuit have considerable knowledge of sea ice. They have a highly developed sense of observation, while their polysynthetic language allows them to describe the many different states of ice accurately and appropriately. During the last International Polar Year the Inuit shared their knowledge and expertise, particularly as part of the SIKU project (in addition to being an acronym for Sea Ice Knowledge and Use, *siku* is also the Inuit word for sea ice). Some Inuit have produced illustrated dictionaries of sea ice containing over a hundred terms.

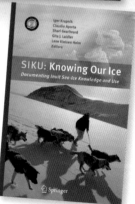

Igor Krupnik
Claudio Aporta
Shari Gearheard
Gita J. Laidler
Lene Kielsen Holm
Editors

SIKU: Knowing Our Ice
Documenting Inuit Sea-Ice Knowledge and Use

Springer

A saw, picks and explosives are employed to try and open the way, 19th century print © arr.

The USS Jeannette crushed by the ice in 1881, 19th century print © arr.

EXPLORERS FROM THE 15ᵀᴴ TO THE 19ᵀᴴ CENTURY

In the late 15th century, explorers started setting out on voyages to the north of the American and European continents, hoping to find new sea routes to China. But polar sea ice was an insurmountable obstacle, causing the loss of many ships and crews. Often these pioneers would get trapped by the sea ice and be forced to overwinter, without adequate equipment or provisions. In 1619, Danish explorer Jens Munk's crew was almost entirely wiped out in Hudson Bay by hunger and scurvy (which is caused by vitamin C deficiency). Only three men survived the winter. In 1719, also in Hudson Bay, all 27 members of an expedition led by Englishman James Knight perished from hunger and sickness.

By the early 18th century, expeditions were better prepared, carrying several years of provisions, including appropriate food to ward off scurvy. Ships now had reinforced hulls and were capable of sliding between drift ice. Sometimes the sailors would even disembark onto the ice to haul their ship through a tricky spot. Or else a hawser would be anchored to the ice then wound to the capstan to winch the ship through. Crews would even open passages in the ice using picks, saws and sometimes explosives. But the sea ice often beat them. In 1829, English explorer John Ross's ship became icebound in the Canadian Arctic Archipelago. Three summers passed without any break-up of the ice. In 1832, the expedition abandoned ship, continued first on foot then by canoe, and survived a fourth winter on the ice before succeeding in returning to England.

In 1845, Sir John Franklin's expedition of two ships (HMS *Terror* and HMS *Erebus*) overwintered close to Beechey Island in the Canadian Arctic Archipelago. In 1846, the ships became icebound in Victoria Strait and were forced to overwinter again. Franklin himself died in June. No break-up in the ice occurred that summer, and by the end of the third winter the expedition had lost 24 men. The 105 survivors abandoned their ships in the spring of 1848 and headed south. All died, from cold, hunger and disease. Some even ate the flesh of their companions.

In 1879, the USS *Jeannette* of De Long's American expedition became trapped in the ice in the Chukchi Sea and drifted for 280 days before being crushed by the ice and sinking, close to the New Siberian Islands. Only nine of the 33 crew who attempted to reach the coast survived

The Hansa crushed by the ice in 1869,
19ᵗʰ century print © arr.

The castaways of the Polaris in 1872,
19ᵗʰ century print © arr.

SHIPWRECKED ON A RAFT OF ICE

In September 1869, the 21-metre German schooner *Hansa* became stuck in the drift ice at 73°N, to the east of Greenland, with 14 men on board. On 18th October, the deck planking buckled under the pressing ice and the ship was pushed up by five metres before the keel broke. The crew escaped onto the ice with what provisions and equipment they could salvage. The *Hansa* finally sank on 21st October at 70°N, and the castaways found themselves on a floe drifting south. They built a hut from charcoal briquettes and succeeded in catching walruses and bears. But each storm reduced the size of their ice raft and nearly threw them all into the sea. In early May 1870, now at 61°N, they abandoned their floe aboard three longboats. Sometimes they were able to sail, otherwise they hauled their craft through the ice. The men were soaked through, exhausted and very soon, starving. On 7th June they finally reached the coast, and a week later an Inuit settlement. The *Hansa* castaways had spent 200 days on a raft of ice that had drifted 1,500 km.

In October 1872, the steamer *Polaris*, of the American Charles Francis Hall's North Polar Expedition, was navigating amid the ice at approximately 78°N, west of Greenland, when she ran aground. A number of the crew were ordered to disembark onto a floe with much of the equipment and supplies, with the aim of lightening the vessel and refloating her. But a break-up of the ice occurred overnight and the *Polaris* drifted off, leaving 19 people stranded on the drift ice, among them the expedition's two Inuit guides, their wives and five children, including a baby. The group had two whaleboats, one kayak, tents, a few provisions and some dogs. The Inuit built igloos and hunted seals and bears, allowing the group to survive the winter. When they ran out of seals, they ate the dogs. In March, a storm split the floe, which was now less than 100 metres long. As the ice opened up more and more, waves began to break over the floe, prompting the group to cram themselves into a whaleboat and seek safety on another floe. But waves washed away their tents, leaving them soaking wet, cold, hungry and thirsty. Finally in late April, off the coast of Labrador, they glimpsed some ships, which an Inuk was able to reach by kayak. The survivors of the *Polaris* were saved after spending six and a half months on the ice and drifting more than 2,000 km.

The Fram in the drifting ice of the Arctic Ocean in 1894 © arr.

Setting-up Ivan Papanin's drifting research station close to the North Pole in 1937 © arr.

THE *FRAM* AND THE DRIFTING RESEARCH STATIONS

The wreckage of the USS *Jeannette* was found off the southern tip of Greenland in 1884, indicating the existence of the Transpolar Drift Stream, and inspiring Norwegian explorer Fridtjof Nansen to cross the Arctic Ocean by drifting on the sea ice. He commissioned the building of the *Fram*, a 39-metre long schooner with a rounded hull 80 cm thick that would ride up over the ice. In September 1893, the *Fram* was allowed to freeze into the ice off the coast of Siberia. Nansen and his 12 companions made various scientific observations as they drifted, discovering that the Arctic Ocean is 3,800 metres deep in places and that warm currents exist at depth. The *Fram* reached the record latitude of 85°55'N and Nansen and Johansen left the ship in February 1895 for the North Pole, reaching 86°13'N and establishing there was no land in the vicinity. They made the treacherous return journey across the drift ice, first on foot, then by kayak, to Franz Josef Land where they spent the winter before being rescued in 1896. As for the *Fram*, it was finally released from the sea ice close to Spitsbergen in August 1896 after drifting for three years.

In May 1937, the Russian explorer Ivan Papanin and three companions landed by plane on the ice close to the North Pole. Camping under canvas, they took meteorological measurements and transmitted them by radio, using a wind turbine to provide electricity. They discovered there were phytoplankton beneath the ice, made bathymetric readings down to 4,400 metres, took water samples at different depths and detected that warm currents from the Atlantic flowed as far as the Pole. During the summer, snowmelt flooded their camp, then as autumn set in, it grew colder and snow buried their tents, making working conditions extremely difficult. By mid-December their floe was three metres thick and 4 km long. They drifted along the east coast of Greenland at speeds close to 50 km a day, but the floe fractured in early February, becoming just 30 metres long. The four men were picked up by a Russian icebreaker at 70°N on 19th February after drifting for nine months. Since then, there have been many drifting research stations set up on the sea ice, as well as on ice islands of land origin. Established primarily by the Soviet Union (later Russia), the USA and Canada, these stations have not only enabled the study of sea ice and the Arctic Ocean, but also allowed oil prospecting on the continental shelves.

Salomon Andrée's balloon on the sea ice in 1897 © arr.

Roald Amundsen's seaplane on the sea ice in 1925 © arr.

POLAR AIRCRAFT

On 11th June 1897, the Swedish explorer Salomon Andrée, accompanied by Nils Strindberg and Knut Frænkel, took off from Spitsbergen in the hot air balloon *Örnen* (Eagle), their destination: the North Pole. The hydrogen-filled balloon became progressively weighed down by frost and ice and was forced to land on the sea ice at 82°56'N after just 65 hours of flight. The three men had provisions, sleds and a canoe, but were 320 km from the nearest land. They began a difficult journey across the drifting ice, their pace slowed by the summer snowmelt. Come September, they resigned themselves to wintering on the ice and built a small hut with walls of packed snow. But in early October, the ice began to break-up, leaving them sitting on a floe just four metres long. They managed to reach the uninhabited glacier-covered White Island, to the east of the Svalbard archipelago. But within days the three men were dead, in circumstances that remain a mystery, because despite their situation, they still had provisions and equipment. Their bodies were discovered 33 years later, along with their journals and undeveloped photographic film.

In 1925, the Norwegian explorer Roald Amundsen, famous for having been first to reach the South Pole in 1911, attempted to reach the North Pole by plane, accompanied by the American Lincoln Ellsworth and four other men. They left Spitsbergen aboard two Dornier Wal seaplanes. After flying over pack ice for eight hours, and with half their fuel gone, the expedition made ready to turn back. But one of the engines on Amundsen's seaplane began to stutter and they were forced to make an emergency landing on a polynya. The expedition had reached 87°43'N but found themselves in a perilous position, with both seaplanes sitting on a polynya that could close up at any time. One aircraft was damaged, and the other was jammed against a hummock. Their only hope was to drag the undamaged 4.5 ton seaplane onto the ice, then haul it several hundred metres over ridges and fractures to a relatively flat floe from where they could take off. The men had nothing but axes, knives and an anchor with which to hack at the ice to clear a path. Then they had to slave for 24 days to cut a runway 500 metres long by 12 metres wide through thick wet snow that lay one metre deep. It took them seven attempts before they were able to take off and return to Spitsbergen.

On 9th May 1926, Americans Richard Byrd and Floyd Bennett took off from Spitsbergen in a Fokker and returned 16 hours later declaring they had flown over the North Pole, an exploit that is disputed.

On 11th May 1926, Italian aeronautical engineer Umberto Nobile took off from Spitsbergen aboard his airship *Norge*, accompanied by Amundsen and Ellsworth. They flew over the North Pole and landed in Alaska two days later, making the first aerial crossing of the Arctic Ocean.

On 23rd May 1928, Nobile took off from Spitsbergen in the airship *Italia* with a team of 15 men. They reached the North Pole the next day, but *Italia* couldn't land because of high winds and they were forced to turn back. A combination of bad weather and technical problems caused *Italia* to hit the sea ice at 81°N. One man was killed on impact and another eight men, including Nobile, were thrown overboard. The airship, its weight suddenly reduced, swept back into the air and disappeared forever with the six remaining crew. The survivors sent a distress signal by radio, and 16 ships, 22 planes and nearly 1,500 men from six nations were mobilized to join the rescue effort. An aircraft spotted the survivors on 20th June and dropped equipment and provisions for them. A Swedish plane succeeded in landing on the ice and taking off with Nobile on board. But when the plane returned for the others, it crashed. The Soviet icebreaker *Krasin* finally succeeded in rescuing the survivors, who had spent 49 days on the ice. The expedition lost eight men, while the rescue mission claimed six lives when a French Latham 47 seaplane disappeared on 18th June with Amundsen and five others on board.

The first landing at the geographic North Pole was by three Soviet planes in April 1948.

Today, most polar ships use helicopters to spot a route through the ice, and to transport passengers and supplies. Planes fitted with skis can land on fast ice or floes of level ice, while aircraft fitted with a traditional undercarriage can land on sea ice if a suitable runway has been created. Caterpillar-tracked vehicles are used to clear or tamp down snow and flatten the surface of the sea ice.

The airship Italia *leaving Spitsbergen in 1928 © arr.*

A Lockheed LC-130 fitted with skis © Anthony Gibson, National Science Foundation

POLAR SUBMARINES

In 1870, the French writer Jules Verne imagined a ship, the *Nautilus*, capable of travelling underwater and fitted with electrical propulsion and tanks of compressed air. In the course of an extraordinary journey, the *Nautilus* ventured beneath the Antarctic sea ice and surfaced by breaking through the ice using a ram fixed to its prow.

The crew of an American nuclear-powered submarine check the hull after surfacing through the sea ice in the Arctic Ocean © U.S. Navy

American submariners take their first steps on the ice after surfacing through the sea ice in the Arctic Ocean © U.S. Navy

In 1931, the Australian Sir Hubert Wilkins aimed to reach the North Pole by journeying beneath the ice. At the time, submarines travelled mainly on the surface, since their combustion engines required an inlet of air. They submerged for brief periods only, running on electrical motors powered by batteries that had to be recharged on the surface. Wilkins thought that the underside of the sea ice was flat and that a submarine with an appropriately shaped upper part could skate along it before surfacing in a fracture or a polynya. He acquired a submarine from the American Navy, modified it and named it *Nautilus*. After many trials and tribulations, the *Nautilus* finally reached the polar sea ice but was unable to slip beneath it, possibly owing to sabotage, for its dive planes had disappeared.

In 1941, a Russian submarine attempted to escape a German blockade by diving under ice on the Baltic Sea. It spent 36 hours under the ice but did not succeed in breaking through and surfacing, and had no choice but to turn back.

In 1954, the first American nuclear-powered submarine, also called *Nautilus,* was launched. She had a fuel range of over 100,000 miles and was equipped with oxygen generators. An inertial guidance system was developed for her, since a traditional compass cannot be used to navigate to the North Pole, owing to magnetic interference. An upward-pointing sounder was also fitted, to determine the thickness of the ice. In August 1957, *Nautilus,* commanded by William Anderson, made the first dive under the Arctic sea ice and discovered that the underside of the ice was not flat, as Wilkins had thought, but uneven, with protruding **ice keels**, some of which jut down 15 to 20 metres. In June 1958, *Nautilus* attempted to cross the Arctic Ocean from the Pacific to the Atlantic. But the ice-covered Bering Strait was too shallow for *Nautilus* to navigate underwater, since the submarine risked hitting an ice keel or an iceberg. So they waited a month for the sea ice to retreat and *Nauti-*

Sir Hubert Wilkins's submarine, the Nautilus, *with its upper deck shaped to skate along the underside of the ice, 1931 © arr.*

An American nuclear-powered submarine surfaces through
the ice of the Arctic Ocean © U.S. Navy

lus was able to reach an area deep enough to dive and progress safely. On 3rd August 1958, *Nautilus* became the first vessel to pass underneath the geographic North Pole. The crossing of the Arctic Ocean below the sea ice took 96 hours.

Another American nuclear-powered submarine, the *Skate*, was given the mission of surfacing on the Arctic Ocean using openings in the ice. It was a delicate manoeuvre given that the submarine had to make a vertical ascent aiming for a small opening, while avoiding ice keels that could damage its hull and compensating both for currents and the drifting sea ice. In the summer of 1958, the *Skate*, with Commander James Calvert at the helm, surfaced in this way a total of nine times. The following March the *Skate* returned to the Arctic Ocean, this time tasked with surfacing by smashing through the underside of the sea ice. As well as an upward-pointing sounder, an array of cameras and lights was installed on her deck so the crew could view the **ice canopy**. The technique involved finding an area of thin ice called a **skylight**, which could be the site of a recent fracture or a polynya covered in young ice. The submarine then made a slow ascent, bringing the top of the conning tower into gentle contact with the ice, and eventually breaking through. On 17th March 1959 the *Skate* became the first vessel to surface at the geographic North Pole by breaking through ice 30 cm thick. During this mission, the *Skate* succeeded in surfacing nine times using this technique.

The successes of the *Nautilus* then the *Skate* proved that the Arctic Ocean was now a military arena in its own right, where submarines could travel undetected and surface to launch their missiles. Since 1959, nuclear-powered submarines, mainly American and Russian, have continually patrolled beneath the sea ice, and each year some of them surface at the geographic North Pole. But in addition to performing their role as a military deterrent, these submarines also collect data of great value to science. Millions of soundings have revealed the topography of the Arctic Ocean floor as well as the thickness of the sea ice. This precious data has revealed a decrease in the thickness of the sea ice over the last few decades.

Surveying the frozen beauty of the polar landscape after surfacing through the ice of the Arctic Ocean © U.S. Navy

IMO 9152959

The Russian nuclear-powered icebreaker 50 Let Pobedy
© *N. Savelyev, PAV*

ICEBREAKERS

In 1864, the Russian merchant Mikhail Britnev had the idea of modifying a small tug, the *Païlot*, with a rounded bow and a strong propulsion system so the vessel could ride up onto the ice and break it with its weight. The modern icebreaker was born. In 1871, the first European icebreaker, *Eisbrecher I*, entered service on the Elbe. In 1881, the *Isbrytaren I* began to operate from the port of Stockholm. Up until 1898, icebreakers were only used on rivers, lakes or in ports, but in 1899, the *Ermak,* designed by Russian admiral Stepan Makarov, became the first icebreaker to navigate the drift ice of the Arctic Ocean, covering 250 miles of sea ice to the north of Svalbard. That same year the 88-metre icebreaker ferry SS *Baikal* came into service, carrying entire trains across Lake Baikal between two sections of the Trans-Siberian Railway.

In the early 20th century, Russia built a fleet of icebreakers to open up navigation routes north of Europe. These new ships were fitted with front, rear and side ballast tanks to make the vessels roll and so be more effective at breaking the ice.

LE « YERMAK » EN MARCHE DANS LA BAIE DE CRONSTADT.

The Yermak © *arr.*

93

In 1928 the *Krasin* became famous for the role it played in the rescue of the Nobile expedition and that of the liner *Monte Cervantes* close to Svalbard, later that same year. In 1932, the *Alexander Sibiryakov* made the first crossing from Archangel to Yokohama in the same season. In 1934, the *Fyodor Litke* made the first crossing from Vladivostok to Murmansk in 83 days, opening the way for a future trade route. During the Second World War, icebreakers cleared the shipping lanes for the Arctic convoys. It was around this time that the first electric-powered and diesel-engine icebreakers appeared, the latter boasting propulsion of 12,000 hp.

In 1957, the first nuclear-powered icebreaker, the *Lenin*, took to the seas. It was four times as powerful as a diesel-powered icebreaker, and energy autonomous for several years.

On 17th August 1977, the nuclear-powered icebreaker *Arktika* became the first surface vessel to reach the North Pole.

The Swedish icebreaker Oden © *Larry Larsson, U.S. Navy*

The Russian nuclear-powered icebreaker 50 Let Pobedy © *arr.*

Modern icebreakers have protected propellers at the front and rear, azimuth thrusters, and their hulls are either coated in a special paint or lubricated with a heated liquid to reduce friction with the ice.

There are now around a hundred icebreakers in service worldwide. Russia has 36, six of which are nuclear-powered. Canada has 18, Sweden and Finland nine. Many icebreakers are river vessels, but one-third of the global fleet operate in the Baltic Sea, and the most powerful Russian icebreakers ply the Northern Sea Route. Various classification systems for icebreakers have been developed by particular countries or shipping companies, determining their area of operation according to thicknesses and types of ice.

The largest nuclear powered icebreaker is currently the *50 Let Pobedy* (50 years of Victory). Launched in 2007, it is 160 metres long, 30 metres wide, with a 75,000 hp propulsion system and a top speed of 21 knots. Two nuclear reactors drive three electric engines, each producing 18 megawatts of power. The ship can break through ice two to three metres thick, and carries a crew of 140 with additional room for 128 passengers. Winter sees the *50 Let Pobedy* clearing the way for merchant vessels on the Northern Sea Route, while in summer it takes passengers to the North Pole.

Exploring a floe, 2ⁿᵈ September 2007, Greenland Sea

Disembarking onto the fast ice, 17ᵗʰ December 2012, Antarctica © Christian Genillard

TOURISM

It's an extraordinary experience to navigate these frozen waters, let alone walk on the sea ice. Every summer, tourists have the chance to join expedition cruises, usually heading north from Spitsbergen, and discover the sea ice and the wildlife that live on and under it. The swell eases as the sea ice appears and a different world opens up to the curious traveller. Ships with reinforced hulls break the thinner floes and push aside the thicker ones, progressing through an amazing landscape; a mosaic of ice floes in their countless forms, of turquoise meltwater puddles, of pressure ridges, and hummocks.

The spectacle of floes cracking then fracturing under the ship's bow, and the sound of ice scraping or striking the hull is fascinating. From the safety of the boat, passengers can observe ivory gulls, seals and polar bears in their natural habitat. Zodiac outings into the middle of the drift ice allow passengers to get closer to the wildlife, and as long as the floe is big enough and strong enough, they can experience the excitement of walking on the sea ice.

Cruises leaving Spitsbergen sometimes go as far as 82°N. Tourists wishing to explore higher latitudes and even reach the geographic North Pole can board a nuclear-powered icebreaker departing Murmansk. Expedition cruises to northeast Greenland provide the opportunity to navigate amid the oldest drift ice in the Arctic as it leaves the Arctic Basin via the Fram Strait. There are also cruises to the sea ice off northwest Greenland and the Canadian Arctic Archipelago.

In winter, planes and helicopters fly to Camp Barneo, a seasonal arctic ice station, and the basecamp for tourist excursions to the North Pole.

On the other side of the world, expedition cruises to Antarctica bring tourists close to penguins, seals and leopard seals on the sea ice.

Golf on the sea ice, Uummannaq, Greenland © World Ice Golf Championship

Diving under the sea ice, Arctic Ocean © Benoit Poyelle, DeepSea Under The Pole by Rolex

SPORTS

The Inuit have long used fast ice as a sports ground, with dog sled or snowmobile racing a favourite pastime. In Greenland, many Inuit play football. But most small communities don't have a sports pitch, meaning footballers have to wait for the sea ice to form each year so they can play on the ice.

Since 1997, an international golf tournament has been held on the fast ice near the town of Uummannaq in Greenland, 600 km north of the Arctic Circle.

Many sportspeople are attracted by the Arctic Ocean drift ice. A large number of them come with the aim of walking, skiing, dog-sledding or snowmobiling to the geographic North Pole. Some leave from islands in the Canadian Arctic Archipelago. Others reach the sea ice by plane or helicopter. A few even dive beneath the ice. Each year since 2002, a temporary base called Camp Barneo has been established on a floe close to the Pole. An airstrip is built to receive planes such as the Antonov An-74, which can carry 52 passengers. Camp Barneo is the starting point for trips to the Pole as well as for the North Pole Marathon, which takes place on the snow-covered sea ice and consists of a 4.2 km loop to be completed ten times in average temperatures of -25 °C. The record time is 3 hours and 36 minutes. It's also been the venue for other sporting events, such as mountain bike racing.

In Quebec, ice canoeing is popular, and races have been held on the St. Lawrence River since 1894. Competitors alternately push their canoes across frozen parts of the river and paddle the rest, dodging blocks of ice. It is quite a spectacular event!

*Camp Barneo on the sea ice
near the North Pole © arr.*

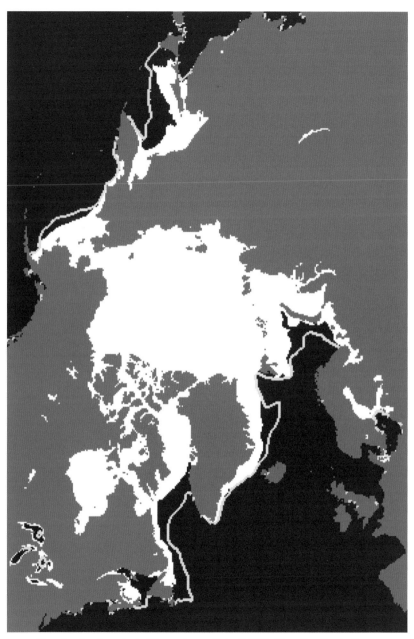

Map showing the extent of the sea ice on 4ᵗʰ April 2006. The yellow line indicates the average ice limit for early April, calculated over the period 1979 -2000
© National Snow and Ice Data Center, USA

THE DECLINE OF ARCTIC SEA ICE

SEASONAL SEA ICE

Satellite observations made since 1978 indicate a decrease in the surface area of seasonal sea ice in the Arctic. The average surface area of the seasonal sea ice in March, when it is at maximum extent, has decreased from 16.2 to 14.7 million km^2 in 34 years, an average decrease of 44,000 km^2 a year.

This decrease has been observed mainly in the Atlantic, on the southeast coast of Canada, the west coasts of Greenland and Spitsbergen, and in the Barents Sea.

The seasonal sea ice is decreasing not only in surface area but also in thickness. According to a study published in 2009 (Kwok and Rothrock) the average thickness of the sea ice dropped from 3.6 metres in 1980 to 1.9 metres in 2008. The thickness is decreasing more and more rapidly, with a loss of 0.6 metres recorded between 2004 and 2008.

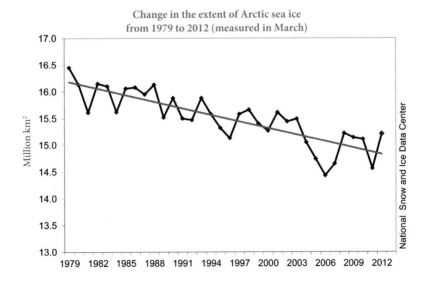

Change in the extent of Arctic sea ice
from 1979 to 2012 (measured in March)

PERENNIAL SEA ICE

Satellite observations made since 1978 indicate a decrease in the surface area of perennial sea ice in the Arctic. The average surface area of the perennial sea ice in September, when it is at minimum extent, has decreased from 8 to 4.9 million km^2 in 34 years, an average decrease of 91,000 km^2 a year. The surface area of the perennial sea ice reached historic minimums of 5.6 million km^2 in 2005, 4.3 million km^2 in 2007 and 3.4 million km^2 in 2012.

This decrease in surface area has been mainly observed to the north of Alaska and Siberia.

The perennial sea ice is decreasing not only in surface area but also in thickness. The oldest ice, and therefore the thickest, continues to decrease. The proportion of ice more than five years old has decreased from nearly 30% to less than 5% over thirty years. In 1988, the surface area of ice more than five years old was over 2 million km^2. In 2012 it was barely 125,000 km^2.

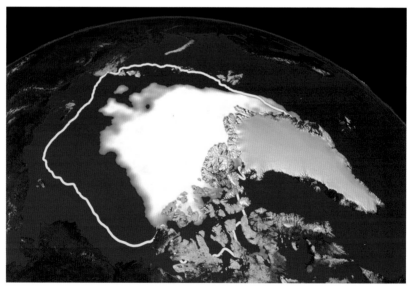

Image showing the extent of the sea ice on 16th September 2012. The yellow line indicates the average ice limit for September, calculated over the period 1979 -2000
© NASA / Goddard Scientific Visualization Studio

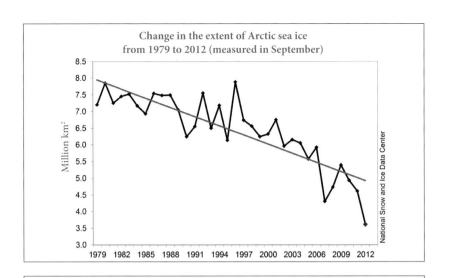

Change in the extent of Arctic sea ice from 1979 to 2012 (measured in September)

National Snow and Ice Data Center

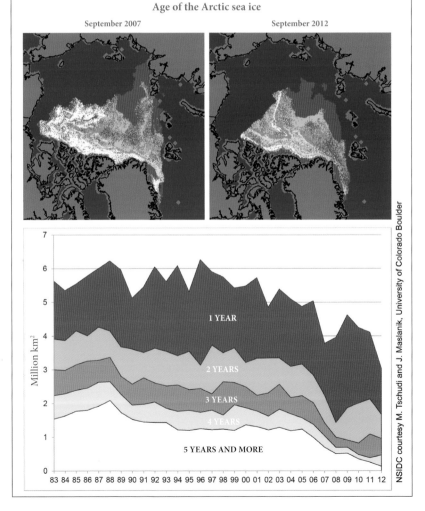

Age of the Arctic sea ice

September 2007   September 2012

1 YEAR

2 YEARS

3 YEARS

4 YEARS

5 YEARS AND MORE

NSIDC courtesy M. Tschudi and J. Maslanik, University of Colorado Boulder

MECHANISMS

The average surface temperature of our planet increased by around 0.74 °C over the course of the 20th century. The Arctic is the region that has experienced the strongest and fastest global warming over the last thirty years. The decrease of Arctic sea ice is both a consequence and a cause of the warming of this region.

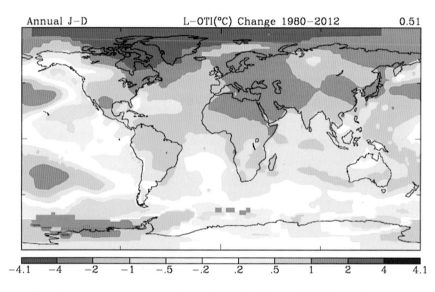

Chart showing temperature anomalies on the surface of the Earth for the period 1980-2012 compared with the norm for 1951-1980 © NASA Goddard Institute for Space Studies

One of the mechanisms involved is the increase in the amount of solar energy captured by the Arctic Ocean. The sea ice acts as a reflector of solar energy, so any decrease in its area, or melting of snow on its surface, results in increased warming of the ocean. A warmer ocean over the summer means that the sea ice forms later in the autumn, is thinner in winter and disappears earlier come spring. The less sea ice there is, the more the ocean warms. The more the ocean warms, the less sea ice there is, a feedback process that amplifies the warming of the Arctic.

Another mechanism related to declining sea ice is the movement of drift ice; the thinner drift ice moves faster under the effect of winds and currents. In the late 19th century, Nansen's *Fram* took three years to drift from the New Siberian Islands to Spitsbergen. Over a hundred years later, starting in 2006, it took the *Tara* less than year and a half to make a similar voyage.

Other mechanisms are linked to weather conditions. During the summer of 2007, the combination of a persistent anticyclone over the Beaufort Sea and a depression in Siberia generated winds that helped to evacuate much more ice from the Arctic Ocean into the Atlantic. In August 2012 a very deep depression generated strong winds over the Beaufort Sea that helped to fracture the drift ice, disperse it and accelerate its melting. 200,000 km² of sea ice disappeared in five days. Unfavourable weather conditions can therefore accelerate the decrease of perennial sea ice.

The future

Most of the warming of our planet over the last fifty years is attributable to the increase in greenhouse gas emissions of human origin. Climate simulations based on current and future greenhouse gas emissions suggest that our planet will warm by 1 to 6 °C by the end of the 21st century. These simulations also show that the Arctic will experience the most pronounced warming, with a decrease in the surface area and thickness of seasonal sea ice and a disappearance of the perennial sea ice.

The perennial sea ice is already growing less thick and more and more fragile. It is estimated that by 2030 it will have disappeared entirely, and with the kind of unfavourable weather conditions seen in 2007 and 2012 it may be lost as early as 2015.

CURRENT CONSEQUENCES

Qeqertaq is a small Inuit community on an island in Disko Bay, Greenland, where the climate warmed by 3.5 °C between 1988 and 2008. The surface area of practicable fast ice decreased from 3,500 to 70 km^2, and the period it could be used, which previously was eight months, is now just a few days or weeks. This massive decrease has had a range of cultural, economic and health impacts.

Many families have given up their dog sleds, because it is no longer economically viable to feed the dogs all year round only to use the sled for a few days during the winter. This cheap means of transport has been replaced by motor-driven canoes, which are costly to run and maintain.

The loss of sea ice has led to a loss of traditional knowledge, because it is rarely possible for skills to be handed down from one generation to the next through practical instruction on the ice.

Fishing has become less profitable. Nets and lines placed beneath the sea ice were once out of harm's way, but are now often carried off by icebergs floating on the open water.

Declining sea ice has made hunting less profitable too. Seals used to be caught all winter long, even during the two months of polar night, using nets placed underneath the sea ice. Now they must be hunted from canoes on the open water, which is far less fruitful.

Inuit and dog sled on rotten sea ice, Qeqertaq, Greenland

Effect of coastal erosion, Shishmaref, Alaska © arr.

Food is more expensive and less healthy. Because of the lack of seal meat, the Qeqertamiut need to rely on imported foodstuffs, which are not only costly, but can also create new health problems.

Access to fresh water is less reliable. Where once the sea ice trapped icebergs, making it possible to hack off blocks of ice to melt for fresh water, the lack of sea ice now means waiting for the winds and currents to bring iceberg debris onto the island's shores.

The craft of conditioning animal skins and making winter clothes for use on the sea ice is being lost.

The community can no longer undertake dog-sled excursions together to visit other settlements across the sea ice, nor can they enjoy community games on the ice.

In the little community of Shishmaref, situated on an Alaskan island, the coast was protected from coastal erosion by seasonal fast ice. Warming of the climate, melting of the permafrost and the decline of the sea ice have resulted in an increase in coastal erosion to the extent that several homes have been destroyed and the community is considering moving.

Boat, fog and icebergs, 2006, Disko Bay, Greenland

Scrawny polar bear, July 2010,
Svalbard © Laurent Balp

Decreasing sea ice exposes more of the ocean surface to the atmosphere, increasing the formation of fog. This affects air traffic at coastal airports, and makes navigation through the iceberg-crowded seas more treacherous.

The decreasing sea ice has also had an impact on the harp seal population, particularly in the northwest Atlantic. The absence of the spring sea ice in their reproduction areas close to Newfoundland and Labrador in 2008 meant the females couldn't give birth on the ice, causing a drop in the harp seal population in this region.

Sea ice decline is causing a fall in the polar bear population. Their principal prey is seal, which they hunt only on the ice. Less sea ice means fewer opportunities to eat, and females who can't build their fat reserves are no longer in a fit state to reproduce. The retreating sea ice can also trap bears on islands, leaving them without sufficient food resources, and forcing the starving animals to eat each other. Bear populations in the Hudson Bay and the Beaufort Sea have already decreased by more than 500 individuals since 1987. In their hunt for food, starving polar bears are no longer wary of approaching humans, causing conflicts that present a danger to both species.

Retreating perennial sea ice in the Arctic Ocean has also affected shipping. Since 2007, the Northern Sea Route has been temporarily free of ice in summer and the navigation season is getting longer year on year. Russia opened this sea lane to international shipping in 2009, and in 2012 nearly fifty vessels took the Northern Sea Route from Europe to Asia.

Ships on the Northern Sea Route © arr.

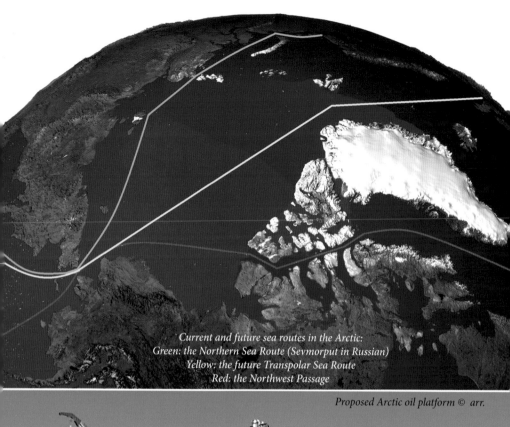

Current and future sea routes in the Arctic:
Green: the Northern Sea Route (Sevmorput in Russian)
Yellow: the future Transpolar Sea Route
Red: the Northwest Passage

Proposed Arctic oil platform © arr.

FUTURE CONSEQUENCES

Climate: the decrease in surface area and thickness of seasonal sea ice, and the disappearance of perennial sea ice will increase the amount of solar energy captured by the Arctic Ocean, resulting in warming and regional climate change, with possible climatic consequences for the entire northern hemisphere.

Economy and geopolitics: the decline of the sea ice should encourage economic and industrial development in the Arctic, with the tapping of oil reserves on the continental shelves, mining, the building of port infrastructures and an increase in shipping between Europe and Asia, initially via the Northern Sea Route, then by the Transpolar Sea Route over an increasingly long summer period. These developments will benefit countries bordering the Arctic, particularly Russia.

Ecology: the economic and industrial development of the Arctic will have consequences for an environment already made fragile by climate change.

Peoples of the Far North: economic and industrial development and environmental changes in the Arctic will affect the peoples of the Far North, particularly the Inuit.

Coastal erosion will increase, affecting landscapes, infrastructure and communities, as well as archaeological sites.

The polar bear will see its habitat disappear over the increasingly long summers, and its populations dwindle. It may become a more continental species, perhaps leading to the evolution of a hybrid species through contact with the brown bear (*Ursus arctos*).

The massive annual phytoplankton bloom might occur earlier in the spring and no longer coincide with the migration period of certain animal species towards higher latitudes, so provoking an upset in the Arctic food chain.

Éditions de l'Escargot Savant - Le Thillot - 21230 VIÉVY France
christian@grandsespaces.ch / +33 380 84 89 91
www.escargotsavant.fr

This book is available from the publisher at a price of € 12 (+ shipping)

Text: Pierre TAVERNIERS
Translation: Roland GLASSER
Photographs: All photographs are by the author unless stated otherwise
Design and layout: Richard SIBLAS with the assistance of Pierre TAVERNIERS
Prints and illustrations: according to sources cited
Maps: Adrien HORNY
English copyediting: Darren KISNER
Printing: ORTHDRUK, Bialystok, Poland - 2013

ISBN: 978-2-918299-26-4
EAN: 9782918299264

Hummock, 28th November 2011, Adélie Land, Antarctica © Bertrand Limouzy

Back cover:
Sea ice on the Arctic Ocean, 21st August 2005. © d.r.